FOLENS
IDEAS BANK
ANCIENT EGYPT

Sally Elding
Rachel Prior

Contents

Folens Publishers

How to use this book

Ideas Bank books provide you with ready to use, practical photocopiable activity pages for children **plus** a wealth of ideas for extension and development.

TEACHER IDEAS PAGE   PHOTOCOPIABLE ACTIVITY PAGE

Clear focus to the activity.

Suggestions for developing work on the photocopiable pages.

Background information and other help given.

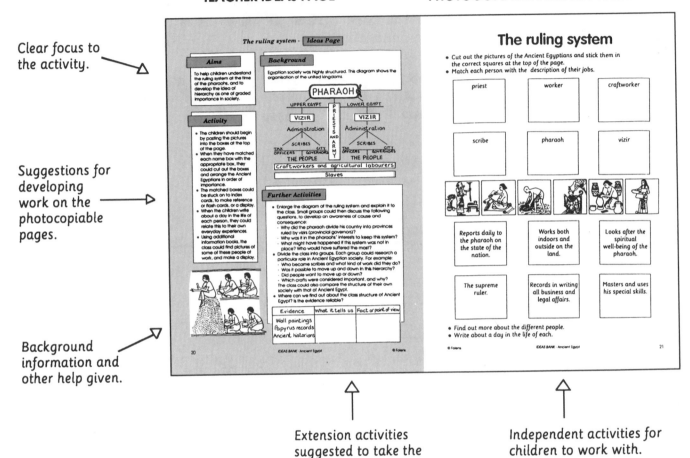

Extension activities suggested to take the work one stage further.

Independent activities for children to work with.

- Time saving, relevant and practical, **Ideas Bank** books ensure that you will always have work ready at hand.

© 1995 Folens Limited, on behalf of the author.

Editor: Joshua Dubin.

Layout artist: Patricia Hollingsworth.

Cover by: In Touch Creative Services Ltd.   Illustrations by: Jane Bottomley.   Cover photograph: The Bridgeman Art Library, Egyptian Museum, Cairo.

First published 1995 by Folens Limited, Albert House, Apex Business Centre, Boscombe Road, Dunstable, LU5 4RL, England.

ISBN 1 85276646-8

Printed in Great Britain at Ashford Colour Press Ltd.

Introduction

Ancient Egyptian civilisation emerged in the Nile Valley over 5,000 years ago. More than 30 dynasties ruled this powerful empire from its unification in 3110BC, under King Menes, until its fall to the Roman Empire in AD30. Ancient Egyptian culture was highly sophisticated, with advanced systems of writing, construction, art and science, some of which have not been equalled to this day. Its archaeological remains still fascinate us, and Ancient Egypt continues to inspire creativity in many fields. Such a wealth of culture allows us great scope for historical investigation and enquiry.

Themes

The purpose of this book is to provide teachers with background information, activities and approaches to a study of the land and people of Ancient Egypt. The contents have been grouped into six themes:

The Land of Ancient Egypt focuses on the location of Ancient Egypt, its important geographical features and the role these have played in Egypt's long history.

The Pyramids concentrates on the design and construction of the pyramids, and the people connected with these well-known landmarks.

The Pharaohs looks at some of the important rulers of Ancient Egypt and the way in which Egyptian society was organised. It also examines the life of Hatshepsut, an activity which can be extended to form a case-study in historical investigation.

Religion investigates the beliefs of the Ancient Egyptians and the impact of these beliefs on their lives.

Everyday Life is concerned with food, leisure, work and fashion.

The Legacy considers some of the links between Ancient Egypt and the modern age, in particular Howard Carter, hieroglyphics and discovered artefacts.

Historical enquiry

The Ideas Pages give essential background information and suggest whole-class, group and individual activities. They also provide developmental ideas. This book aims to guide children in their study of history, and in particular:

- investigating sources
- asking and answering questions
- making comparisons
- interpreting evidence
- developing a sense of chronology
- using reference material
- acquiring factual knowledge
- presenting findings.

Activity focus:

The Land of Ancient Egypt:
- Locating information on a map.
- Using a key.

Annual flooding:
- Representing historical information about the Nile.

Links with other places:
- Egypt's connections with other countries.

The development of the pyramid:
- Arranging the sequence of design development in chronological order.

Inside the pyramid:
- Identifiying the interior elements of a pyramid.

The pyramid builders:
- Using picture clues to identify occupations.

Rulers of Egypt:
- Interpreting historical information.

Hatshepsut:
- Using stories and historical sources.

The ruling system:
- Understanding information in order to represent the structure of society.

The gods:
- Identifying gods and goddesses from pictorial sources.

How the world became:
- Using a story to gain historical understanding.

Life after death:
- Researching and presenting information on the afterlife.
- Learning through game-playing.

Mummification:
- Asking and answering questions.
- Research.

In the garden:
- Research and design.

Toys and games:
- Researching and presenting information on pastimes.
- Learning through game-playing.

Ancient Egyptian army:
- Interpreting historical evidence.

Fashion:
- Interpretation of historical evidence.

Measurement:
- Investigating Ancient Egyptian timekeeping and measurement.

Howard Carter and Tutankhamun:
- Speaking and listening.
- Role play.

Hieroglyphics:
- Interpreting source material.
- Design.

The map - Ideas Page

Aim

To enable children to locate Egypt and its surrounding area on a map.

Background

Over 90% of Egypt is covered by desert, which was often referred to as the Red Land, and was not easily habitable. The River Nile was (and is) a major influence on the daily lives of the people. In ancient times, most of the population occupied the area on the banks of the river, the *Kemet* or *Black Land*, named after the dark silt that remained when the flood waters receded. This was where the farmers grew their crops.

Activity

- Use world maps to locate Africa and more specifically Egypt. Relate it to the child's own country in terms of distance and direction.
- They could design a suitable key, as indicated on the activity sheet, and use it to label the map.

Further Activities

- Discuss with the children why the people from surrounding countries found the inhabitants of the Nile Valley difficult to attack.
- What could some of the problems have been in governing such a country? Think about:
  - the size of the country
  - the amount of desert area
  - the possible methods of travel.
- How might the pharaohs have tried to solve some of these problems? The children should give their reasons.
- Herodotus (450BC) called Ancient Egypt 'The Gift of the Nile'. The children could discuss the importance of the river and compare their answers. Does the River Nile have the same functions today as it did in the past? The children could collate their information on to a chart.

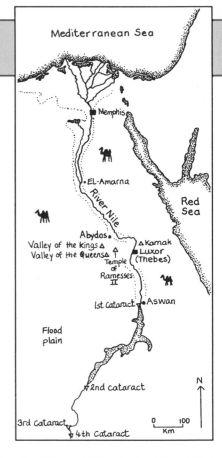

Function	Value	Then	Now
Water source			
Inundation			
Communication			
Transport			
Natural barrier			
Food source			

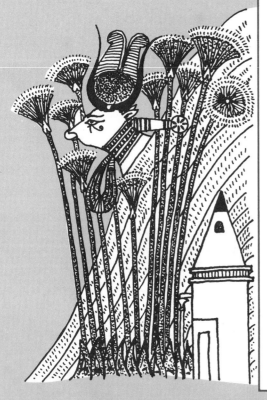

The Land of Ancient Egypt

- Below is a map of Egypt. Use books and maps to help you find all the places listed.
- Complete the key for the places using the symbols. Mark them on the map.

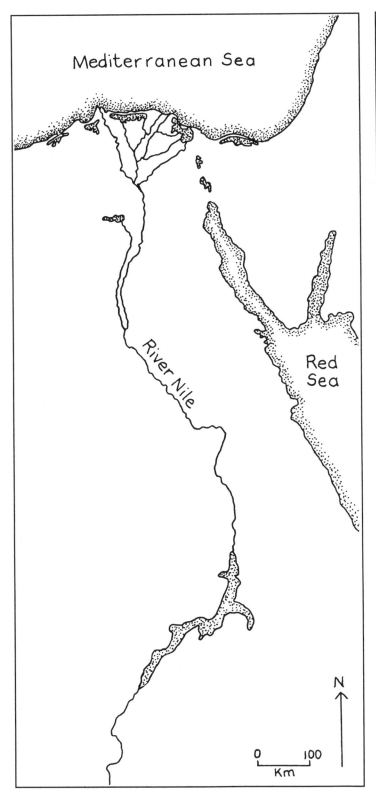

Key	
Memphis	
Thebes	
El-Amarna	
Luxor	
Aswan	
Abydos	
Valley of the Kings	
Valley of the Queens	
Temple of Ramesses II	
Karnak	
Flood plain	
Desert	
Cataracts	

Aim

To develop an understanding of the annual flood cycle of the River Nile and its impact on the lives of Ancient Egyptians.

Background

The lives of Ancient Egyptians were dominated by a three-season year. Every year, rain and melting snow from the high regions of what is now Ethiopia swept down the Nile Valley, causing the river to overflow. As the waters receded, rich black silt was left behind. The livelihood of Egyptians depended on this yearly cycle.

Crops were grown on the fertile soil to provide food and drink (beer) and to pay taxes to landowners. Farming stopped and during the flood season many people worked instead on projects such as the pyramids.

Further Activities

- Pose 'cause and consequence' questions, for example:
  - If the waters of the inundation rose too high, what would happen to the houses near the Nile, to the people in the houses, to their fields and crops and to their lives in the following year?
- Ancient Egyptians believed that the flood waters came from the bottomless jar of the god Hapi, who sat below the mountains of Aswan protected by magic serpents. Can the children discover other flood or inundation myths?

Culture or religion	Story
Judaism Christian Muslim Greek Aborigine	Noah

- Why do people seek to explain significant events like floods by inventing stories or myths?

Activity

- Give the children the following information about the agricultural calendar.

Name	What happens	Calendar months
Akhet	The waters of the Nile overflow and flood the fields on the banks of the river. No farming.	July/August to November
Peret	The water level goes down. The land is ploughed and crops planted and cared for.	November to March
Shemu	Harvesting time. Crops are gathered. Irrigation channels dug and repaired.	March to July/August

- On the activity sheet, using words and pictures, children could represent this information on the wheel diagram. The middle circle could show the movements of the Nile and the outer circle the agricultural process. They could also write the names of the Egyptian seasons by the Western months they correspond to. The circle could be made into three separate discs, fixed with a paper fastener and spun to match the information on the three circles.

Annual flooding

Links with other places - Ideas Page

Aim

To show children that the Ancient Egyptians traded with other countries.

Background

The Nile was crowded with boats of many sizes carrying goods to and from other nations. Memphis and Thebes were great centres of trade. Goods traded in Egypt came from Africa, the Middle East and the Mediterranean lands. Egyptian artisans often adapted other countries' goods to local tastes and materials. Evidence from artefacts found in other cultures shows that Egyptian goods were sold in foreign markets.

Further Activities

- Discuss what may have been traded when the merchants brought their goods home. Set up an imaginary market based on wall paintings, such as that below showing trading booths on the quay at Thebes. Role-play using debens (weights made from copper and other metals; see pages 38-39) and bartering. For example:
  - You have come from Africa with ebony to sell. You are willing to trade it for linen. Barter for a fair price.
  - You are an Egyptian with rolls of linen to trade. You are looking for any goods as long as you receive a fair exchange.

Activity

- Children could use an atlas to locate the countries on their map. On the activity sheet, they could mark each product on its country of origin, draw a possible trade route from there to Egypt, measure the distance and complete the table.
- What questions do the children now want to ask about trade in Ancient Egypt? (For example, were there alternative trade routes to Egypt?) What information were they unable to find? How could they discover the answers?

Source of information	What it tells us	Is it reliable?
Wall painting		
Weights		
List of goods		
Ships' logs		
Historians		

- What sources of information do we have about trading in Ancient Egypt, apart from atlases and history books? Make a chart like the one on the left.
- Discuss and list problems Ancient Egyptian ships might have faced while sailing long distances for trade.

Links with other places

● Complete the chart below. Mark on the map the countries and their products. For each product, draw a possible trade route to Egypt.

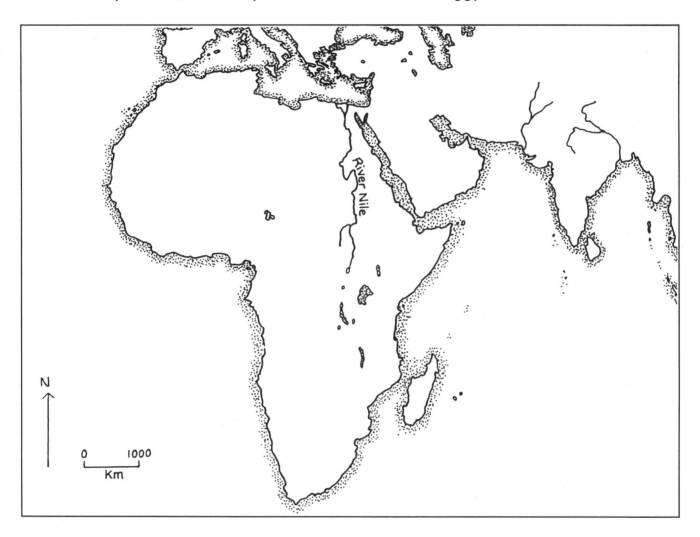

Product	Country	Distance	Possible use
Laurel trees	India		
Incense, timber	Punt (Eritrea)		In the temple
Copper, opium	Cyprus		
Silver	Greece		
Ivory, baboons, lions, animal skins	Africa		
Olive oil	Crete		
Timber, silver	Syria		
Lapis lazuli	Babylonia		

IDEAS BANK - Ancient Egypt

The development of the pyramid -

Aim

To demonstrate the development of design and technology in pyramid-building.

Background

The pyramids of Egypt are the oldest stone buildings in the world, and probably the largest tombs made by people. The earliest Egyptian graves were very simple and easily robbed of their funerary offerings. In an attempt to prevent this, the pharaohs built mastabas: rectangular, flat-topped buildings over burial chambers. However, this did not stop the thieves, so layers were added on top of the mastaba to make it even safer. This is thought to have influenced the step pyramid built for Imhotep (2667-2648BC), probably the clearest design for the true pyramid. It appears triangular because the steps have been filled in. Explain that the 'traditional' pyramid was the final stage in the structure's development.

The pyramids were built on level ground and for religious reasons placed on the west bank of the Nile - the side on which the sun sets.

Activity

- The children could:
  - cut out the diagrams and arrange them in order from the earliest design to the latest
  - find out where examples of these designs can be found
  - research the approximate dates of the pyramid developments and make a time line, pasting the pictures on in chronological order.

Further Activities

- Research other aspects of the pyramids, for example construction and its problems.

Building:
- how long did it take to build a pyramid?
- what tools did the workers use?
- who built the pyramids?

- Present the following statements to the children and ask them to say whether they are true, false or an opinion.
  - All pyramids were built on the west bank of the Nile.
  - Only pharaohs had pyramids.
  - The gods watched over the building of the pyramids.
  - Imhotep designed the step pyramid.
  - Many pyramids have been destroyed by vandals.
  - The pyramid at Giza took only five years to build.
  - There are remains of over 90 pyramids in Egypt.
- The children should recognise that it is due to lack of evidence that we do not know exactly how the pyramids were built.

How did the workers move the materials:
- to the site?
- into position?

From mastaba to pyramid

- Read the descriptions of the different types of pyramid.
- Match each description with the drawing.

True pyramid

The tomb was built on a square base. The steps were filled and faced with limestone, giving it a smooth surface.

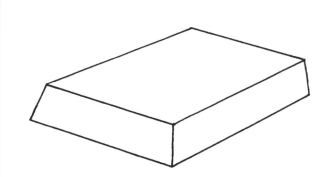

Step pyramid

Layers were added to the mastaba, giving it the appearance of a four-sided staircase.

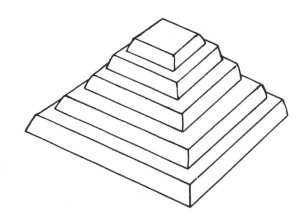

Mastaba

A flat-topped, rectangular building was erected over a burial chamber.

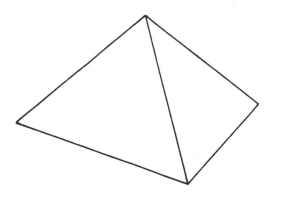

- Find out when these were built. Cut them out and put them on a timeline.
- Why did the design of pyramids change?

Aim

To understand the interior structure of pyramids, and the reasons behind these designs.

Background

The pyramids of Egypt were vast funeral monuments. Often the burial chambers they contained were little more than vaults, to which access was gained by narrow passages.

Inside the Great Pyramid of Cheops at Giza, the builders made a series of passages leading to the king's burial chamber. This entrance was concealed by a large granite slab and some of the passages were either so low that visitors had to wriggle along on their stomachs, so narrow that it meant shuffling along on their knees, or set at a steep incline.

A French consul-general in Egypt published the first cross-section of the pyramid of Cheops in 1735. He described the interior as dim and blackened from candle smoke. Of the stones, he marvelled at the precision of the joins, so perfect that even a knife blade could not be slid between them. Protection against robbers was a major concern of the pyramids' designers.

Other chambers in the pyramids would have been included for members of the monarch's family, for religious or ceremonial purposes, or for temporary use by contruction workers.

A wealthy Egyptian's tomb was likely to contain valuable artefacts, including:
- furniture, jewellery and other everyday artefacts
- *shabtis* (statuettes of the noble's workers and overseers)
- charms and amulets, usually of precious metals and stones
- food (sometimes modelled in wood or clay) for the deceased to eat in the afterlife.

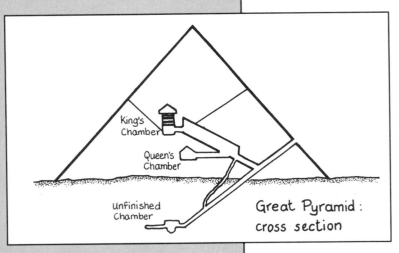

Great Pyramid : cross section

Activity

- The children could decide where to locate the named features, mark them on the cross-section and label them.
- They could then write a simple description of their route through the pyramid.
- Discuss the reasons for the complicated design of a pyramid (in order to discourage tomb robbers).

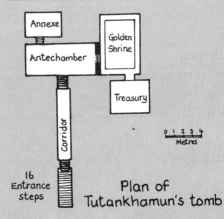

Plan of Tutankhamun's tomb

Further Activities

- Children could compare the route through the pyramid with one they might take through Tutankhamun's tomb.
- Perform a role play, where one or more children try to find their way through the chambers of a pyramid in order to steal its contents. Create a pyramid interior in the classroom, using masking tape or chalk and tables and chairs. Make models of *shabtis* and other artefacts that might be found in a noble's tomb, and place them in appropriate places in the classroom pyramid. Other characters could be introduced, such as architects, soldiers or even the God of the Dead, who try to protect the tomb.
- Find and locate remaining tomb and pyramid sites in Egypt today and mark these on a base map (see page 5).

Inside a pyramid

- Label the features of this pyramid using the words below.

  Mark a route from the entrance (A) to the burial chamber (B) .

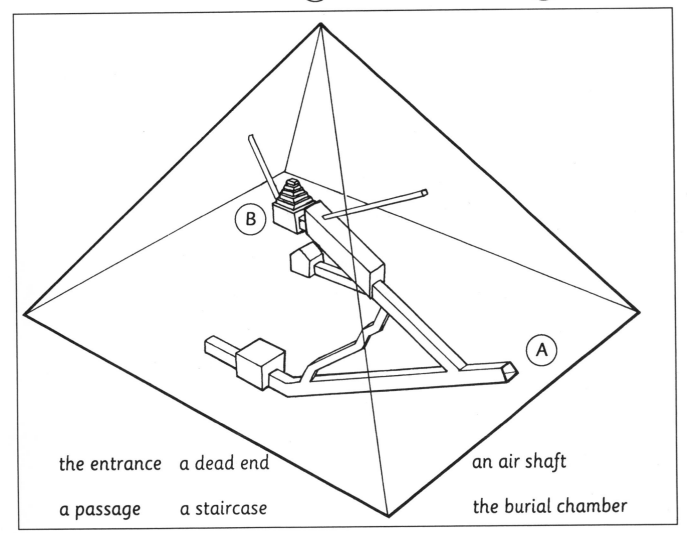

the entrance   a dead end   an air shaft

a passage   a staircase   the burial chamber

- What problems might tomb robbers have encountered? Write them below.

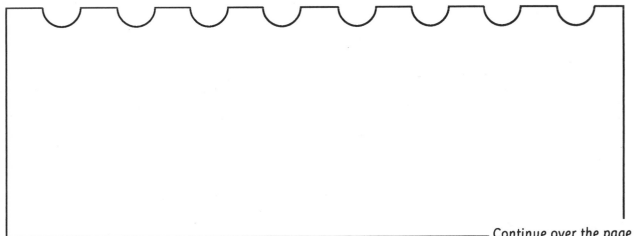

— Continue over the page ...

The pyramid builders - Ideas Page

Aim

To consider some of the different roles and skills of the pyramid builders.

Background

A vast army of people was required to build the pyramids, including architects, stonemasons, floor-layers, carpenters, decorators and painters. The theory that the pyramids were built by slave labour has been disproved. It is now recognised that they were built with a conscripted labour force.

The remains of the village of Deir el Medina near Luxor (which housed craftsmen and artists who decorated tombs for almost 500 years) has provided evidence and information about work gangs, tools, techniques and materials.

Activity

- Ask the children to identify the job of each of the workers from the clues given and give their reasons:
  - model pyramid and correspondence: an architect
  - mallet, chisel and wedges: a stonemason
  - string, grid plan and paint: an artist
  - stone block, food and drink: a manual worker.
- Ask the children to explain how each clue has led them to their answer.
- They could then find out more about the work involved in each job, and could compare this to similar work today.

Further Activities

- Consider what materials were used to make tools in Ancient Egypt, and why they were chosen. What materials were available? For example, iron and copper were rarely used, as these metals were imported. Compare these tools with ones that we can buy today. Make a chart that shows the similarities and differences between tools then and today. Do the same for site machinery such as cranes and diggers.
- Explain that our knowledge of Ancient Egyptian crafts comes from tools which have been discovered by archaeologists, and from wall paintings, such as the one shown below, which depict workshops. The children should be aware that this evidence alone may not provide all the information they need to answer their questions about pyramid-building. What other kinds of information would they need for their research?

- Invite local craftsmen to school to explain their jobs and the tools that they use.
- Ask the children to look at a grid like the one on this page, which shows the proportions used by Egyptian artists and craftsmen. They could copy other figures using this grid. Does the grid give an accurate diagram of human proportions? How could the children find out?

The pyramid builders

In each of the boxes below are some clues to help you
identify a person who worked on the pyramids.

- Under each box write what you think each person's job was.

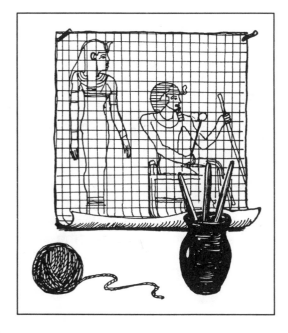

- On the back of this sheet describe what each person did.

Hatshepsut

Aim

To introduce some of the important rulers of Ancient Egypt and the stories and developments associated with them.

Tutankhamun

Background

The word 'pharaoh' is derived from *perao* meaning 'great house'. Pharaohs ruled over two distinct regions: Lower Egypt, based around the delta of the Nile and represented in paintings by a ruler with a red crown, and Upper Egypt, centred around Abydos in the south, represented by the white crown. According to legend, about 3000BC the two regions were united under one crown, often shown as a double red and white headpiece. Referred to as the Old Kingdom, this era saw the emergence of pyramid-building and hieroglyphs. From 1580BC onwards there was a period of great power: the New Kingdom, which witnessed rulers such as Akhenaten, Hatshepsut, Tutankhamun, Tuthmosis and Ramesses.

Activity

- The children will need a copy of 'The Pharaohs' Who's Who' (page 46) or other information books.
- They should study each of the 'fragments' and link each visual clue with a ruler of Ancient Egypt. They should give their reasons.
  Answers: asp–Cleopatra; double crown–Menes; sun rays–Akhenaten.
- A fourth fragment has been left blank. The children could draw in it a symbol to represent another pharaoh, which they could choose and design for themselves.

Ramses II wearing the Double Crown and carrying the flail and crook.

Further Activities

White crown of upper Egypt   Red crown of lower Egypt

- The children may wish to draw more 'fragments' for other rulers of Egypt. These could be made into individual, group or class 'Guess Who' books.
- The children could gather information about the pharaohs of Ancient Egypt and present this either on a database or as a simple matrix or time line. They could add events from the history of other cultures to their time line, so that they can understand Ancient Egypt's location in time.
- Ask the children to consider the different kinds of crowns and symbols that the pharaohs wore and used, and to think about why these symbols were chosen.

	Lower Egypt	Upper Egypt	Reasons
Crowns Animals Plants	red cobra papyrus	white vulture lotus	

- Collect pictures of different pharaohs and ask the children to identify key features of the portraits, sculptures or masks.
  - Why did pharaohs want to be portrayed with such features?
  - If the children had only one picture to look at, what conclusions would they draw? Why?
  - Show children other pictures, for example one of Akhenaten.
    How is this different? What does it suggest about using historical sources?
- The children could consider other symbols of authority and their significance, for example the menes, the crook and flail, and the false beard.

Rulers of Egypt

- Look at the fragments of wall paintings below.
- Use books and other resources to help you to decide which ruler each fragment represents and why.

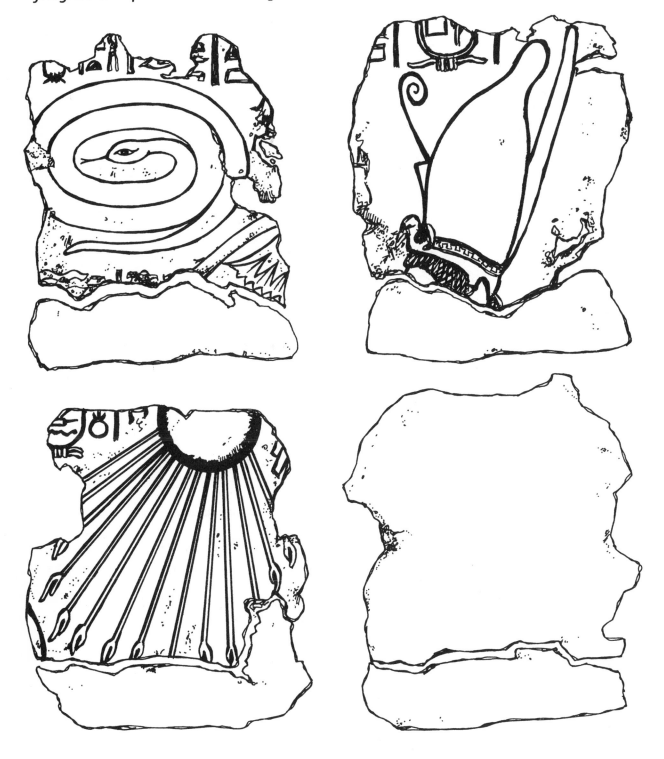

- Choose a design to represent another Ancient Egyptian ruler.
- Draw it in the fourth fragment.

Queen Hatshepsut - Ideas Page

Aim

To learn the story of the birth of Hatshepsut and to consider how evidence may not provide all the information needed to make valid deductions.

HATSHEPSUT

Background

In the land of the gods, Ra the sun god called a meeting of all the gods and spoke of his desire to make a great ruler who would rule over the entire lands of Egypt. Thoth, the god of knowledge, listened with interest to the words of Ra and in the silence that followed he told of a maiden of wondrous beauty, the wife of the king of Egypt. She alone would be worthy of being the mother of such a great ruler. Ra was interested to see this woman for himself and so asked Thoth to take him and all the gods to see her. Silently, for it was night-time, the gods and goddesses entered the palace and were guided by Thoth to the chamber of the queen. There, Aahmes the queen lay asleep, and as they gazed upon her they saw that what Thoth had said of her beauty was indeed true. Their presence, however, woke Aahmes but she listened as Ra told her of his plan. Then Ra invoked the power of the god Khum, the creator of life. So it was that Aahmes gave birth to a daughter, Hatshepsut, who became a great ruler of Egypt.

Activity

- Tell the story of the birth of Hatshepsut.
- Ask the children to complete the activity sheet.
- Encourage the children to make detailed drawings, and to use colours. Invite them to describe what they will draw before they fill in each square on the sheet. Ask questions such as: Where is Ra standing? What is he wearing? How tall is he? What is he looking at?

Further Activities

Tuthmosis I
1504 – 1492 BC

Tuthmosis II
1492 – 1479 BC

Hatshepsut
1479 – c.1425 BC
Regent with her nephew then ruler.

Tuthmosis III 1479 – 1425 BC
Tried to erase Hatshepsut from history by defacing her monuments and adapting them as his own.

- Groups could be asked to make a 'still' photograph of any scene from the story as a drama activity. The class could ask questions of any person in the photograph. For example, they could ask of Thoth: 'How did you come to know about the mother of Hatshepsut?', and of Ra: 'Why did you choose Aahmes to be the mother of a great ruler?'
- Explain to the children that Hatshepsut reigned first as a regent queen for her nephew, Tuthmosis III, and later as a pharaoh in her own right, after usurping the throne. We believe that she invented the story about her descent from the gods. Ask the children to discuss why she felt it necessary to make up the story, and why she made herself a pharaoh.
- Explore Tuthmosis III's reasons for removing Hatshepsut's name from her monuments and destroying references to her. Perform a role play with the children. Aside from Tuthmosis III, characters might include Hatshepsut, Tuthmosis I, Tuthmosis II, and other influential people such as vizirs and priests.

Tuthmosis III

Hatshepsut

- In the boxes below draw the story of Hatshepsut's birth.
  The first one has been done for you.

Ra tells the gods that he wants a
new ruler.

Thoth knows someone who could
be mother to such a ruler.

One night all the gods went to see
this woman while she was asleep.

The woman, Aahmes, who was
very beautiful, woke up.

Aahmes listened to what Ra had
to say and agreed to his plan.

Aahmes gave birth to Hatshepsut,
who became a great ruler.

The ruling system - Ideas Page

Aims

To help children understand the ruling system at the time of the pharaohs, and to develop the idea of hierarchy as one of graded importance in society.

Background

Egyptian society was highly structured. This diagram shows the organisation of the united kingdoms.

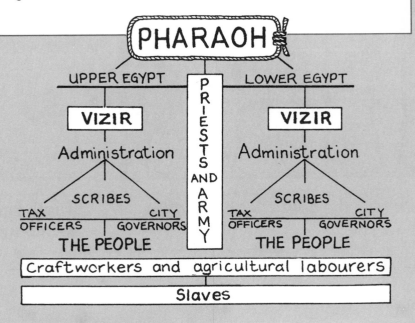

Activity

- The children should begin by pasting the pictures into the boxes at the top of the page.
- When they have matched each name box with the appropriate box, they could cut out the boxes and arrange the Ancient Egyptians in order of importance.
- The matched boxes could be stuck on to index cards, to make reference or flash cards, or a display.
- When the children write about a day in the life of each person, they could relate this to their own everyday experiences.
- Using additional information books, the class could find pictures of some of these people at work, and make a display.

Further Activities

- Enlarge the diagram of the ruling system and explain it to the class. Small groups could then discuss the following questions, to develop an awareness of cause and consequence:
  - Why did the pharaoh divide his country into provinces ruled by vizirs (provincial governors)?
  - Why was it in the pharaohs' interests to keep this system?
  - What might have happened if this system was not in place? Who would have suffered the most?
- Divide the class into groups. Each group could research a particular role in Ancient Egyptian society. For example:
  - Who became scribes and what kind of work did they do?
  - Was it possible to move up and down in this hierarchy?
  - Did people want to move up or down?
  - Which crafts were considered important, and why?
  The class could also compare the structure of their own society with that of Ancient Egypt.
- Where can we find out about the class structure of Ancient Egypt? Is the evidence reliable?

Evidence	What it tells us	Fact or point of view
Wall paintings		
Papyrus records		
Ancient historians		

The ruling system

- Cut out the pictures of the Ancient Egyptians and stick them in the correct squares at the top of the page.
- Match each person with the description of their jobs.

priest	worker	craftworker

scribe	pharaoh	vizir

Reports daily to the pharaoh on the state of the nation.	Works both indoors and outside on the land.	Looks after the spiritual well-being of the pharaoh.

The supreme ruler.	Records in writing all business and legal affairs.	Masters and uses his special skills.

- Find out more about the different people.
- Write about a day in the life of each.

Anubis

Aim

To familiarise children with some of the gods worshipped by the Ancient Egyptians, and their associated animal attributes.

Activity

- Use the cards and 'The Gods' Who's Who' (page 47) to identify the gods.
- Children could play recognition games, such as Snap, with several copies of the cards.
- One child could place a card in front of another and ask questions such as 'What am I the god of?' 'What is my symbol?'

Bes

Background

Although evidence is incomplete about many of the gods worshipped, we do know that the Ancient Egyptians were a very religious people whose everyday lives were governed by their beliefs. The importance of particular gods varied with time and many deities were revered locally, not universally. For example, a god called Amun, his wife Mut and his son Khons were worshipped locally in Luxor. The pharaohs were also worshipped as gods.
Ancient Egyptian gods and goddesses had animal attributes, often represented by animal heads. For example, Hathor (Ra's daughter) is drawn as a cow tending her calf (motherly love) and also a beautiful woman (sensuality). Sekhmet, goddess of war, is a lioness.

Further Activities

- Children could design and make face masks. They will need 'The Gods' Who's Who' and other suitable reference materials.
- The children could sit in a circle wearing their masks and introduce themselves in role to the group or class. For example, 'I am Anubis, the god of the dead. You can recognise me by my jackal head.'
- Ask the children to choose five gods and discuss what they would pray to them for. They could record this on a chart such as the one below. Ask the children to write a suitable prayer. In Ancient Egyptian times, written prayers would have been left in the temple.

God	Responsibility	Reason for prayer
Osiris	God of king's afterlife	To ensure the king reached the fields of reeds.

- This picture shows a ceremony called 'the opening of the mouth'. Use pictures like this to ask the children questions, such as:
  - What do you think is happening?
  - How can you identify the priest?
  - How and why is he dressed specially?
  - What is on the table? Why?
  - Which is the dead person?
  - Who is holding the mummy?
  - What are the young girls doing?
  At each stage, the children should be challenged to give reasons for their answers.

The gods

- Find out the names of these Ancient Egyptian gods and goddesses and write them below each picture.

- Now find out more about them.

Aim

To introduce the children to a version of the Ancient Egyptian story of the creation of the world.

Thoth, the god of wisdom and scribe to the gods.

Background

Creation stories abound. It is worthwhile pointing out to the children that they may encounter not only variations of the Ancient Egyptian story of creation, but differing accounts of the creation from across the world. For instance, the early Egyptians told three different stories about how their world began:

1. Thoth, the god of wisdom and scribe to the gods, created the world himself.
2. Ra the sun god was responsible for its creation.
3. Ptah was the creator of everything.

Many children will already be familiar with a creation story from their own culture which may be similar to other creation stories.

Ptah, the creator of everything.

Activity

- Give either the text or the pictures to the children to arrange in sequence. Those with pictures could be asked to write their own text to match. Children with the text could draw their own pictures.

Ra
The sun god.

Further Activities

- The children could work independently or in groups to think, talk and write about aspects of the story:
  - The dark, empty world before light and life began.
  - The lotus flower: How did it look, feel, smell? How did it open?
  - The baby asleep under cover of the petals.
- They could continue the creation story and provide explanations for the creation of, for example, moon and stars, mountains, waves, crops, trees, clouds and so on.
- This is an opportunity to look at creation stories from around the world. Groups could be asked to research, and collaborate to write, some of these stories for a class anthology.
- A matrix of creation stories from around the world could be the basis of a wall display.
- Investigate how different myths (Egyptian, Chinese, North American Indian, Inuit) explain the creation of the sun, earth, moon, stars, water, wind and fire.

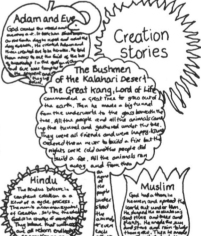

How the world became

Before the world began, nothing existed at all. There was darkness all around. Suddenly, as if from nowhere, a rare and beautiful thing appeared. It was a lotus flower.

Inside the head of this flower a baby slept peacefully and undisturbed. Slowly, gradually, the petals of this flower began to move and to open.

The movement of the petals released a powerful scent. As the scent erupted into the darkness, the baby awoke from its slumber.

As the baby's eyes opened, bright sun rays flashed across the vast darkness. They showed the birth of the sun god, Ra.

Next, as if in an instant, two things happened. The baby was a baby no more and his imagination began to stir. As it did so, the world and all it contained was created.

This giant of a figure looked down to see where he rested and the earth came into being. He raised his eyes upwards and the sky became. As the rays of the sun god, Ra, were reflected back into his eyes, tears rolled down this giant's cheeks and the seas, rivers and lakes were formed.

IDEAS BANK - Ancient Egypt

Aim

To discuss Ancient Egyptian ideas of an underworld and to create a representation of this.

Anubis

Activity

- Introduce the children to the story of what happened to the Ancient Egyptians when they died.
- Using appropriate reference books, they should draw the missing stages of the journeys in the spaces provided.
- They could devise simple rules before they play their game.
- Ask the children to imagine they have taken this journey and have to decide whether they are truthful or not, and complete the final box with an illustration of what might happen to them.

Background

Ancient Egyptians believed that after a dead person had been buried in their tomb, the gods Anubis and Horus guided them through the underworld to the next world, first in a boat across the River of Death – a place of many dangers, such as poisonous snakes, lakes of fire and evil spirits. A map and magic spells, which had been written in a Book of the Dead and also on the coffin, were left with the body to help it reach the Fields of Yaru (Paradise). When recited, the spells would ensure that the person passed by unharmed.

In the Hall of Judgement, Anubis weighed the heart of the dead person against their past deeds. Osiris, god of the dead, and 42 judges would interrogate the dead person, whose heart would hang in the balance against the Feather of Truth. If an untruth was spoken, then the heart would weigh heavier

Osiris

than the feather and would be eaten by the crocodile, Devourer of the Dead. If the person was truthful, then Horus would provide an escort to Paradise. Here a dead person would be required to work in the fields. For those who did not want to work, *shabti* figures, which were buried with the body, would leap to life and do the work instead.

Further Activities

- The children could create large-scale models or drawings of the underworld.
- Find a picture like the one below from Hunefar's *Book of the Dead* (1285BC). Question children about what is happening to test their understanding of this topic.
  - Can the children identify the gods?
  - Who is leading Hunefar towards the scales?
  - What is on each balance of the scales? Why?
  - What is the crocodile Amemet waiting for?
  - Who is writing down what is happening? Why?
  - Who is leading Hunefar towards Osiris? Why?

Life after death

- Complete the gameboard.

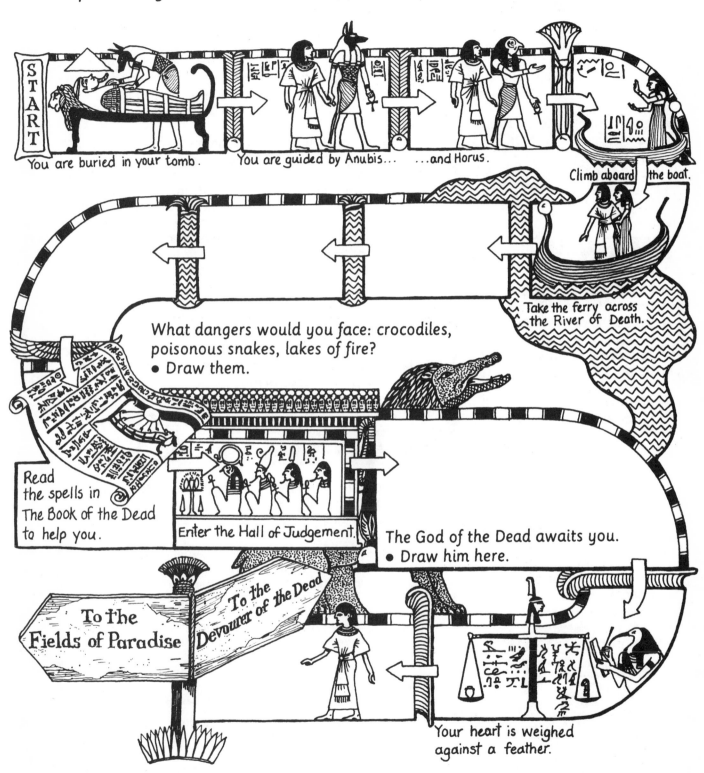

START
You are buried in your tomb.
You are guided by Anubis...
...and Horus.
Climb aboard the boat.

Take the ferry across the River of Death.

What dangers would you face: crocodiles, poisonous snakes, lakes of fire?
- Draw them.

Read the spells in The Book of the Dead to help you.

Enter the Hall of Judgement.

The God of the Dead awaits you.
- Draw him here.

To the Fields of Paradise

To the Devourer of the Dead

Your heart is weighed against a feather.

- Now play your game.
- What happens if you have been untruthful?
- What happens if you have been truthful?

Aim

To introduce children to funerary practices, by asking questions about the ritual process of mummification.

Canopic jars

Activity

- Explain the mummification process to the children.
- Divide the class into groups. Give each one a 'sarcophagus' and ask them to answer its questions. Every member of the group should suggest answers: working together and sharing information is vital. As a whole class, share the information and review the process of mummification.
- Use the sarcophagus outline as a template for a shape-book. Use this to record each stage of mummification.

Background

Mummification is the preservation of a dead body. Ancient Egyptians believed that a physical body was required after death, in order to feed their soul on the food which was left in the tomb. Preserving the body in a lifelike state enabled the soul to recognise its body after death. Written accounts of the process were first made by Herodotus, the Greek historian (4th century BC).

After death, a body was taken to an embalmer's workshop. The internal organs were removed through incisions in the stomach and nose and placed in Canopic jars representing the four gods believed to protect these organs. Imsety, a god in human form, protected the liver. Kebehsenuef, falcon-headed, protected the intestines. The lungs were looked after by Hapi, who had a baboon's head. Jackal-headed Duamutef was responsible for the stomach.

The body was covered for 40 days in crystals of natron, a salt-like substance that dried out bodily fluids. Then the body was washed and the insides packed with linen. The body was wrapped in layers of bandages and coated with oils and resin. The head was fitted with a decorated mask resembling the dead person. Finally the mummy was placed in a wooden or plaster coffin and then in an outer coffin, which would be painted with protective charms.

Further Activities

- Tell the children that, to the Ancient Egyptians, human life comprised three elements.

Ka
A person's spirit double. Symbol: upraised hands. Resembled the owner physically. Left the body at death to travel to the underworld. Returned to the entombed body at sunrise.

Ba
An individual's life force. Symbol: a human-headed bird. Left the body at death and returned at will. The recognisable body was necessary for the *ba* to perch on.

Akh
The ghost. Exists only in the afterlife. This is what the *ka* becomes if it is well cared for.

- Why was a preserved body necessary?
- What would have happened to the *ka* and *ba* if there had been no body?
- The survival of the *ka* and *ba* meant immortality for the person. Why was this so important? (See pages 26–27.)
- Why were false doorways built into the walls of the tombs near the mummies?
- Why was it important for the mummy to bear a resemblance to the person in life by wearing a mask?

Mummification

Figure 1:
- Why did the Ancient Egyptians want to preserve the body of a dead person?
- How do we know about the process of mummification?
- Which god was associated with the ritual of embalming?
- Who was the god of the dead?
- How long did the process of embalming take?

Figure 2:
- What happened to the body after the internal organs had been removed?
- What was applied to the body?
- How long did this part of the process take?
- What effect did this have on the body?
- What was done to the mouth of the dead person? Why?

Figure 3:
- How and why were the internal organs of a dead person removed?
- Which organs were removed?
- What did the embalmers do with the internal organs?
- What happened to the heart?
- What happened to the brain?
- How did the Egyptians find out about preserving the body of a dead person?

Figure 4:
- What was the body packed with before being wrapped in bandages?
- What was applied to the linen bandages and why?
- Where was the body then placed?
- What kinds of decoration were used on the coffin?

In the garden - Ideas Page

Aims

To introduce the range of products grown in an Egyptian garden, and to design and draw a garden containing some of these plants.

Background

Plants were grown in Ancient Egypt not only for food and medicinal purposes, but also for hair and skin colouring, for dyes in paints and for perfume. Where land was available, those who could afford it built spacious villas with gardens, pools and trees. Decorative pools, a central feature of Egyptian gardens, also provided water for irrigation.

Activity

- The children should research the information in order to complete the chart.
- Ask the children:
  - Do we still grow these plants today?
  - Are they grown for the same reasons?

Medicine

aniseed
cornflowers
garlic
linseed
lotus
olives
onions
peppermint
poppies
thyme
willow

Perfume

coriander
linseed
lotus
olives

Dyes

onions
cornflowers
henna
madder

Food

aniseed
apricots
broad beans
celery
chick peas
coriander
cucumbers
dates
figs
garlic
leeks
lentils
lettuce
melons
nuts
olives
onions
peas
pomegranates
radishes
sesame
thyme
vines

Further Activities

- A central feature of the garden was a pool. Why? How were gardens irrigated? The children could investigate how water from a fixed source can be distributed as and when needed. They will need to research sluices, dams, falls and *shadufs*. Which of these methods are used today? Where?
- Children could plan and design gardens, using either a modern or an Ancient Egyptian style, as in this copy of a wall painting.

- Plan an Egyptian meal using some of the foods on the activity sheet. Children could compare their modern meals with Ancient Egyptian ones. Consider where and how the meal was cooked and who cooked it.
- Use onion skins to make dyes. What other plants make dyes? Carry out experiments and make a chart to show what colours can be obtained from different plants. Remember to include the children's predictions.

In the garden

We know that the Ancient Egyptians grew the following plants in their gardens:

> aniseed, apricots, broad beans, celery, chick peas, coriander, cornflowers, cucumbers, dates, figs, garlic, henna, leeks, lettuce, lentils, linseed, lotus, madder, melons, myrtle, nuts, olives, onions, peas, peppermint, pomegranates, poppies, radishes, sesame, thyme, vines, willow.

- Use books to help you find about about these plants. Then complete the chart below.

Grown to eat	Grown for medicine	Grown for perfume	Grown for dyes

- Now design and draw a plan for an Egyptian garden that will grow a range of foods. Provide a key.

Toys and games - Ideas Page

Aim

To design, make, write rules for and play an Ancient Egyptian board game.

Activity

- The children could write a set of rules for the 'Snake' game using the background information.
- The game can be played and tested by other children. Showing the class the rules of a modern game may help them with the presentation of the 'Snake' game rules.

Background

Tomb paintings and artefacts tell us that Ancient Egyptians played board games. One of these is the 'Snake' game, so called because of the playing board. This board varied in size: the larger the snake, the more segments in the body and possibly the longer the game took to play. The game is illustrated in the tomb of Hesy. Under the board is a box of counters and marbles. There were six counters (three hounds' heads and three lions) and six sets of six marbles. This may suggest a game for six players or two teams of three, but how the game was played is unknown.

Further Activities

- Discuss the toys and games that the Ancient Egyptians played with, such as those shown on this page.
- Carry out a survey of the children's favourite games. The information could be entered into a database. Use these details to compare Ancient Egyptian and modern toys and games.

Rules for Senet:
- 7 pieces per player.
- Set out pieces alternately along first 14 squares.
- Move in a reversed-S direction.

- Give the children a list of statements about the Ancient Egyptians and leisure time. Ask them to classify these as facts or points of view. For example:
  - Ancient Egyptians had no fun: they only thought about death.
  - They were too busy building tombs to play.
  - Ancient Egyptians played with toys and games.
- Make some Senet boards and teach the children how to play.
  - Senet was played on a rectangular board divided into three rows of 10 squares. The aim is to remove all one's own pieces from the board while preventing an opponent from doing the same. Moves are determined by throwing a die. If a piece is blocked, it returns to the start.

The 'Snake' game

● Make, write the rules for and play this Ancient Egyptian board game.

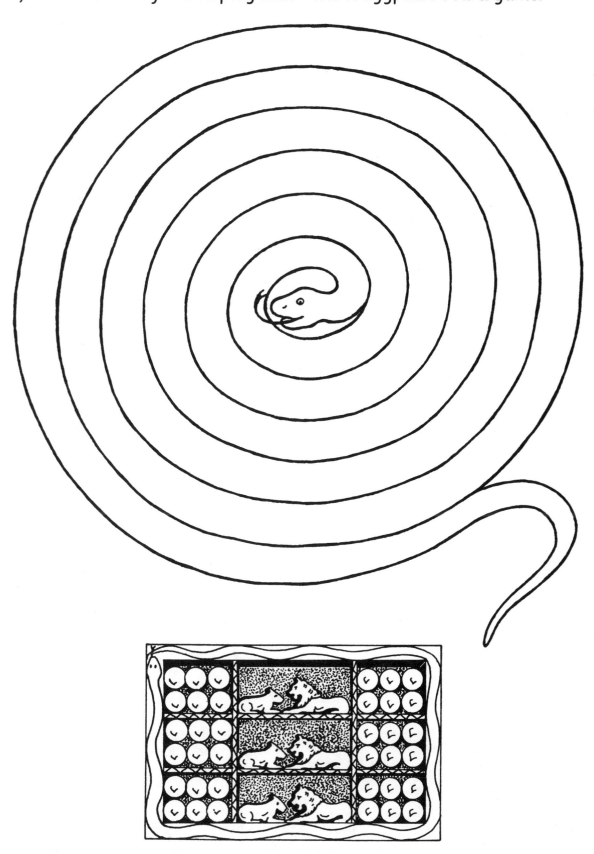

The Ancient Egyptian army - Ideas Page

Aims

To learn about the army in Ancient Egypt, especially in the period of the New Kingdom, and to discuss how historical evidence requires interpretation.

Egyptian pikemen

Background

The army of the New Kingdom was divided into four regiments, each named after a god. A regiment had 20 companies, each with its own standard and 200 men. The companies were divided into four units, 50 men in each, and had 25 two-man chariots. Chariots formed the front of the battle line. Mercenaries were used extensively.

Soldiers wore bands of leather to protect their chests and carried shields. Weapons were made from wood and bronze, and included javelins, axes, maces, swords, bows and arrows.

Activity

- Explain to the children that the illustration on the activity page is a modern drawing based on carvings on the wall of the mortuary temple of Ramesses III (1198–1166BC). This temple, on the west bank of the Nile near Luxor, celebrates the Pharaoh's victories over his enemies, the Libyans. The carving is over 19 metres high. The children could mark the temple on their base map. In the picture, the Libyan soldiers are recognisable by their long garments, sidelocks and beards.
- Children could identify the two armies, then shade and label them.
- Ask questions such as:
  - Why should a king celebrate his victory by having a huge carving made of it?
  - Do rulers do the same thing today?
  - How can we recognise Ramesses, and why is he portrayed larger than anyone else?

Further Activities

- The most famous battle in the history of Egypt was the battle of Kadesh (1285BC), fought by Ramesses II. Kadesh is in northern Syria, and was the stronghold of the Hittites.
- Use the map and the information to fight the battle again. Children could make a large version of the map and models of the various regiments based on the activity sheet.

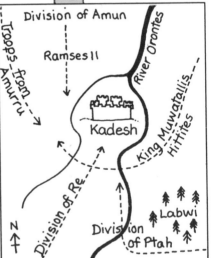

Information

3 Egyptian divisions: Amun, Re, Ptah. Hittite deserters told the Egyptians that King Muwatallis was abroad. Ramesses attacked the Hittite fortress at Kadesh: the King was in the fortress when he attacked. Ramesses fought alone (with his pet lion). The Pharaoh prayed to Amun and won. Egyptian troops from Amurru arrived in time. The Hittites were driven into the river, and then negotiated a truce.

- Look at the map and the information. Discuss the difficulties of the battle. For example, Kadesh was surrounded by two rivers. Is Ramesses' story possible?
- Ramesses II carved this victory on to the wall of a temple, but documentary evidence from Ancient Syria suggests that Ramesses lost the battle (hence the negotiation). What do the children think that this shows about evidence like the wall carving and the way it needs to be interpreted?

Nubian archers

The Ancient Egyptian army

- Look carefully at this copy of a wall painting.
  It shows Ramesses III fighting the Libyans.

- How can you identify the Pharaoh?
- How can you identify the two armies?

Fashion - Ideas Page

Aim

To discuss Ancient Egyptian clothing, hair and jewellery from historical research.

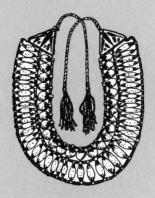

Background

Most Ancient Egyptian clothes were made from linen, as it was light and cool to wear. Perfumes and make-up were thought to have medicinal qualities, as well as making the wearer more attractive. Ancient Egyptians generally had shaven heads, but wore wigs of wool or real hair for religious or other special occasions. Wig designs became more elaborate over time, incorporating beads and jewellery. Children are portrayed with a sidelock (perhaps a symbol of youthfulness) rather than a wig, and are often seen naked.

Jewellery was worn by all classes of Egyptian society. Poor people wore jewellery made from copper and faience (tin glaze). Wealthier people had jewellery made from gold, silver and electrum (a mix of gold and silver), inlaid with coloured glass or semi-precious stones. These expensive pieces included necklaces, rings, bracelets, pendants, belts and anklets, as well as spectacular and colourful beaded collars and pectorals. Pectorals were large items of jewellery worn over the chest or breast, whose designs included 'magical' symbols, such as the scarab beetle.

Most Ancient Egyptians walked barefoot, but sandals made from reeds, or sometimes leather, have been discovered.

Activity

- The children should research what Ancient Egyptians wore. While they are researching, point out that in Ancient Egyptian wall paintings the men are usually portrayed in a darker colour than the women.
- They can then choose whether their template is of a man or woman, and draw on it the appropriate clothes and accessories. Remind them that both men and women wore make-up and jewellery.
- Draw comparisons with today's fashions. What changes or similarities do the children notice? For example, one of the masks of Tutankhamun had pierced ears. Why?

Further Activities

- Ask the children to research areas of fashion, collect data and suggest how reliable the evidence is. For example:
  Hairstyles:
  - Was there a traditional hairstyle?
  - Did the styles change during the Ancient Egyptian period?
  Clothes:
  - Was there a traditional Egyptian style of dress?
  - Did the style change according to wealth, age, occupation?
  - Did they decorate their clothes?
  - What did they wear on their feet?
- How do we know about Egyptian hairstyles, clothes and footwear?

Fashion

- Find out how Ancient Egyptian men and women dressed. Look at the examples of costume and jewellery on this page.

- Decide whether your figure will be a man or a woman. Dress the outline below by drawing on a complete outfit.

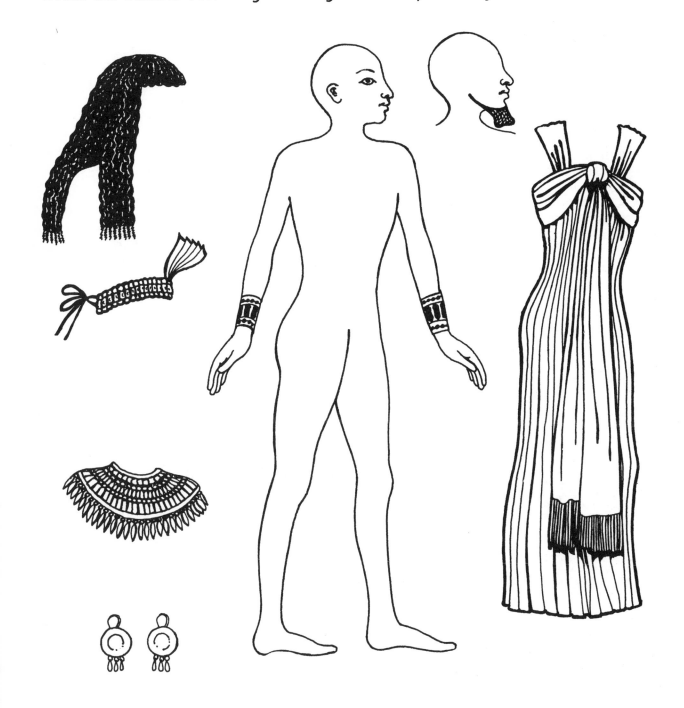

- Now find out how children dressed. How were they different from children today?

digit

Aim

To investigate Ancient Egyptian methods of measurement.

Activity

- Discuss the information with the children to ensure they understand the principle of standard and non-standard measurement.
- Ask the children to research how the measurements might have been used in everyday life in Ancient Egypt.
- Finally, discuss what changes have taken place and why, then complete the 'What we use today' column.

Background

Length: measurements were made using arms and hands. The basic unit was the **hand**, which was four **digits** or fingers wide. A **cubit** was the larger measurement of length. There were two ways to calculate a cubit: the distance from elbow to fingertip, or seven hands (side by side).

Weight: The **deben**, a metal ring of copper, silver or gold, was the standard unit. In other words, debens would be the same weight but different sizes. We know little about how they were used in practice, but it seems that they were not used as coins.

Capacity: Liquids were measured with a series of graded jars.

Time: The Ancient Egyptians developed a water clock. This was a round container, like a plant pot, with a hole in the side and filled with water. Marks inside the container indicated the periods of the time elapsed as the water drained out.

cubit

Numbers

1 year	= 3 seasons
1 season	= 4 months
1 month	= 3 weeks
1 week	= 10 days

Further Activities

Other measurements

Numbers: Enlarge the numbers shown on the left to show the children. They could make mathematical puzzles for each other using this system.

Calendars: The first Egyptian calendar was planned around the stars. Astronomers noticed that Sirius went below the horizon at the same time each year and reappeared 70 days later, and that this coincided with the start of the rising level of the River Nile. The second calendar was planned around the movements of the Moon, which gave the month its length. This lunar calendar set the dates for religious festivals. The third calendar divided the year into weeks, months and seasons; days were divided into 24 hours.

- Children could compare these with the calendar today, and with different calendars used by other religions or cultures.

Seasons

day   month   year

Akhet (Inundation)

Peret (Winter)

Shemu (Summer)

Measurement

- Read and talk about the information below.
- In the right-hand column draw what we use today.

Measurement	Details	What we use today
Volume	Measured in jar sizes: 1 hekat = 4.54 litres 16 hekats = 1 sackful (khar). The average wage for a fieldworker was 1.5 khars of wheat per month.	
Length	Measured in cubits - from the elbow to the tip of the longest finger = 52.5cm; or seven hands side by side = one cubit.	
Weight	A metal ring called a deben weighed 91 grams. One tenth of a deben was a kite.	
Liquids	Liquids were measured in jars. The standard measurement was one hin = 0.5 litres.	
Time	Measured by a water clock. This was a round container with a hole in the side. There were marks inside the container to indicate time.	

- Choose one of these activities:
  - Make an Ancient Egyptian water clock.
  - Design an alternative way of measuring time.

Aim

To introduce the children to some of the characters and events surrounding the discovery of the tomb of Tutankhamun.

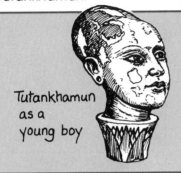

Tutankhamun as a young boy

Background

Lord Carnarvon

Archaeologist Howard Carter, funded by George, 5th Earl of Carnarvon, worked for over ten years on excavations in Egypt, particularly at the Valley of the Kings. On 4 November 1922, when Lord Carnarvon had returned to England and the Egyptian government's period of permission to dig had nearly expired, workmen uncovered a flight of steps leading below ground. They led to a walled entrance bearing the seals of the royal necropolis. Carter knew this was an important discovery. He sent a telegram to Carnarvon, who returned at once. The steps were cleared, a stone screen was removed and a sloping corridor cleared of rubble to reveal another door. On 26 November, by the flicker of candlelight, Carter removed a few stones from this final door. Carnarvon asked, "Can you see anything?" Carter replied: "Yes, wonderful things."

Activity

- Set the scene using the background information.
- Organise the class into groups of four. Give each group a set of the role cards.
- Regroup the class: bring together all those with the same role card. These groups should read, talk and think about their characters.
- The news reporters should formulate a set of questions to ask the other characters.
- When all the children are ready, they should return to their original groups of four. Each group can hold a press conference, at which the reporter can ask his or her questions.

THE WONDERFUL DISCOVERIES IN EGYPT

LORD CARNARVON'S OWN COMPLETE ACCOUNT OF ALADDIN

AT LAST HAVE MADE WONDERFUL DISCOVERIES IN VALLEY STOP A MAGNIFICENT TOMB WITH SEALS INTACT STOP RECOVERED SAME FOR YOUR ARRIVAL STOP CONGRATULATIONS STOP CARTER

Further Activities

- Ask the children to write a diary of events surrounding the discovery of Tutankhamun's tomb, written from the viewpoints of the different characters. Display these with other versions of the story taken from information books. Compare the stories: what differences are there, and why?
- Carter's telegram to Carnavon read: 'At last have made wonderful discovery in Valley. A magnificent tomb with seals intact. Recovered same for your arrival. Congratulations!' Invite the children (individually or in groups) to write the return telegram. These could be printed out using a word-processing program, and displayed alongside a picture of the real telegram.
- The children could research the young king's sarcophagus.
  - Draw a cross-section showing and identifying the all the layers from mummy to outer coffin.
  - Use card or balsa wood to make a model of the coffins' arrangement.

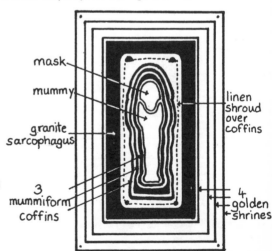

mask

mummy

granite sarcophagus

linen shroud over coffins

3 mummiform coffins

4 golden shrines

Howard Carter and Tutankhamun

Howard Carter

You are Howard Carter, the archaeologist who discovered the tomb of Tutankhamun. Originally a draughtsman, working in Egypt, you are sure that there are great discoveries to be made in the Valley of the Kings. You have already made some significant finds when you meet Lord Carnarvon and his daughter. On 4 November 1922, while Lord Carnarvon is back in England, a workman hits a hard surface in the sand. He runs to tell you, and you uncover some stone steps leading to a doorway marked with a royal seal.

An Egyptian Worker

You are one of the team of workers employed by Howard Carter and Lord Carnarvon. You are there when your fellow workmate runs to Mr Carter and tells him excitedly that he has found something he thinks the Englishman should look at. You help to uncover the sixteen stone steps and see the doorway with the royal seal on it. You help to clear away the rubble from the corridor behind. Finally, you are a witness to the words spoken between Lord Carnarvon and Howard Carter as he takes away a few of the stones from the second door. "Can you see anything?" asks Carnarvon. "Yes, wonderful things," replies Carter.

Lady Evelyn Herbert

You are Lady Evelyn Herbert, the daughter of Lord Carnarvon. Your father spends every winter in Egypt because of his health (his lungs were damaged in a car accident) and he has given Howard Carter the money to work in the Valley of the Kings for the past ten years. Your father receives a telegram from Carter and you both hurry to Egypt, to uncover the secret hidden behind the sealed door. You know everything that has happened and you intend to remain in Egypt to witness the discoveries.

News Reporter

You are a reporter for The Times newspaper. You are on assignment in Egypt and have heard that something is happening in the Valley of the Kings. You have to get your news story. You have heard some whispers about a discovery but nothing has been confirmed yet. When you reach the Valley, you set up a meeting with the people involved. You are to meet Howard Carter, Lord Carnarvon, Lady Evelyn Herbert (Carnarvon's daughter) and a site worker. They know what has happened here. Make a list of the questions you want to ask Lord Carnarvon and Howard Carter about what they have found in the Valley of the Kings. How will you record the replies? What else can you find out from other people, before the interview? How will you conduct the interview?

Aims

To introduce children to the Ancient Egyptian writing system (hieroglyphs) and to discuss some of the problems of deciphering it.

Activities

- Discuss the hieroglyphic alphabet.
  - How is this not like our alphabet?
  - What letters and sounds are missing?
  - What problems could this cause in trying to decipher the alphabet?
- The children could represent their own or other people's names in the cartouche.
  - What letters or sounds were unavailable?
  - How did they overcome this problem?
  - How did they pronounce their names when they were written in hieroglyphs?

Background

The word 'hieroglyph' comes from the Greek for 'holy writing'. The Egyptians believed writing was the 'word of the gods' and that the understanding of the written word was a gift from Thoth, the god of wisdom.

Hieroglyphs were symbols and pictures which represented an object, the sound of letters or sometimes both. There were no symbols for vowels, so there is some disagreement about 'correct' spelling when translating words.

Hieroglyphs can be written and read upwards, downwards, left to right and right to left. The clue is to look for any people or animals in a message and see which way they are facing. If they are facing to the left, then the message should be read from the right to the left. When the name of a pharaoh or important person was written in hieroglyphs it was contained within an oval frame called a cartouche.

Scribes had responsibility for recording information in hieroglyphs (see page 20). Their duties were wide, and even included recording grain harvests.

Further Activities

- The children could research the Rosetta Stone.
- Ask the children to write down three questions they would like to ask about the hieroglyphic alphabet. How could they find the answers to their questions?
- Below is a chart listing the contents of a scribe's kit. Help the children to research the information they will need to complete the chart.

Article	Made from	Use	Picture
Wooden box			
Shoulder strap			
Polished stone			
Palette			
Inks			
Water jar			
Pens	Softened reeds		
Papyrus			

- Draw a copy of this hieroglyph for the children. Discuss with them why it represents a scribe. Draw their attention to the two wells for ink, the shoulder strap, the water pot and the reed pen.

The Rosetta Stone.

Writing

- Below is the hieroglyph alphabet that the Ancient Egyptians used.

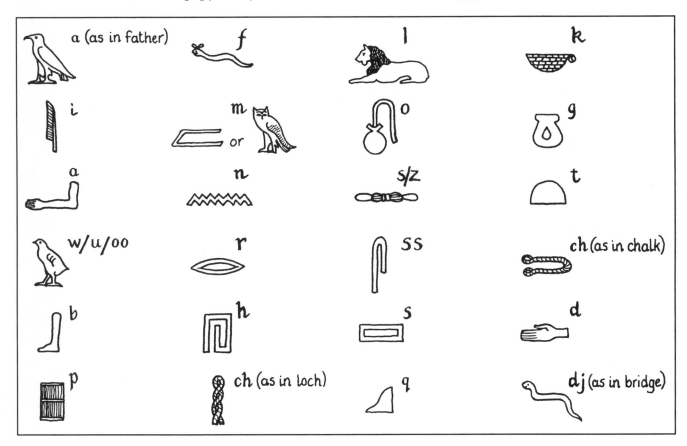

Here is how the names of Ptolemy and Cleopatra were written.

P T O L M II S

K L I O P A D(T) R A

- In the space below, write your name in hieroglyphs.

Aim

To compare present-day artefacts with their Ancient Egyptian equivalents.

Background

The *Chambers Dictionary* defines an artefact as 'a thing made by human workmanship'. We know much about the Ancient Egyptians from the artefacts they left behind. Their pyramids, tombs and temples were like museums, filled with evidence of Ancient Egyptians' lives.

Although many of these buildings were robbed of their belongings, some objects can still be viewed in museums today. Work is constantly being undertaken in Egypt and new discoveries continue to develop our knowledge about this ancient civilisation. The children should be aware that even the most ordinary artefacts can give us a great deal of information.

Activity

- Talk with the children about the information that artefacts can give us about people and their way of life. Tell them how the artefacts from Ancient Egypt reached this part of the world, and that there are still new and important discoveries being made which add to our knowledge. The activity sheet contains drawings of artefacts that we see today in various aspects of our lives. The children should research and then draw their Ancient Egyptian equivalents.

Further Activities

- Create a class museum. Build up a collection using pictures, photographs, handmade replicas and models. Use the activity sheet as a basis for information cards to go with them.
- Which six items would the children choose to show aspects of our lives today to people in the future? Why?
- Use photographs of artefacts and ask them to talk about what they know, what they can guess and what more they would like to find out about the objects.
- Look in detail at one artefact. Use the chart below to create a full profile of the item.

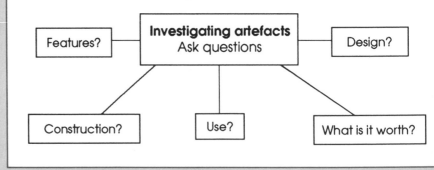

Features? — **Investigating artefacts** Ask questions — Design?

Construction? — Use? — What is it worth?

Artefacts then and now

● In the chart below, draw pictures of Ancient Egyptian artefacts.

	Today we use:	The Ancient Egyptians used:
For cooking:		
For moving objects:		
For communicating:		
For farming:		
For entertainment:		
For building:		
For transport:		
For beauty treatment:		

The Pharaohs Who's Who

Name	Period	Information
Menes (c. 3100BC)	*1st Dynasty 3100BC–2890BC*	The first Egyptian ruler. He unified Egypt, combining the red and white crowns.
Tuthmosis III (1479–1425BC)	*18th Dynasty 1570–1300BC*	Tuthmosis III was a great warrior pharaoh. He enlarged the Egyptian empire to its widest limits. He was said to have been only five feet tall. His grandson was Tutankhamun.
Hatshepsut (1479–c.1425BC)	*18th Dynasty 1570–1300BC*	She ruled for over 20 years. She ordered the building of a temple at Deir-el-Bahri which can still be seen.
Akhenaten (1352–1336BC)	*18th Dynasty 1570–1300BC*	Also known as Amenhotep IV, he Introduced the worship of one god: Aten, the sun god. He built a new capital city. Mystery surrounds his death. His wife was Nefertiti.
Tutankhamun (1336–1327BC)	*18th Dynasty 1570–1300BC*	The boy king's reign began when he was nine years old; he died aged 18.
Ramesses I (1295–1294BC)	*19th Dynasty 1300–1200BC 20th Dynasty 1300–1080BC*	There were at least 11 rulers of this name. Ramesses I (called The Great) started the building programme in the Valley of the Kings and built more monuments and statues than any other pharaoh. The last great warrior king, he fought the Sea People of the Mediterranean.
Alexander (332–323BC)	*Period 332–305BC*	He conquered Egypt and the Persian Empire. He founded many new cities, the most famous of which is Alexandria. He died at the age of 32.
Cleopatra (51–30BC)	*Ptolemaic Period 305–30BC*	The last Greek pharaoh, she married Marc Antony, friend of Julius Caesar. She killed herself with a bite from a snake after the death of Marc Antony.

IDEAS BANK - Ancient Egypt

The Gods Who's Who

Name	Attribute	Symbol
Amun	Creator and king of the gods	Goose/ram
Anubis	God of the dead	Jackal
Bast	Goddess of mothers	Cat
Bes	God of children and marriage	Dwarf
Geb	Earth god	Earth/land
Hapi	God of water and flood	Water/river
Hathor	Goddess of love, happiness music/dancing	Cow
Horus	Keeper of the pharaoh	Falcon
Isis	Goddess of crafts	Wings
Kephri	God who rolled the sun across the sky each day	Scarab beetle
Khonsu	Moon god	Moon
Khumn	Creator god	Ram
Ma'at	Goddess of truth and justice	Feather
Nefertem	God of oils and perfumes	Blue lotus flower
Nut	Goddess of the sky	Sky
Osiris	God of death and the underworld	Figure wrapped in bandages
Ptah	Creator of the universe	Bull
Ra	Sun god - giver of life	Hawk/sun
Renenutet	Goddess of the harvest	Snake
Sekhmet	Goddess of war	Lioness
Set	God of evil, desert and storm	Ass/pig
Shu	God of air	Wind/air
Sobek	God of water	Crocodile
Taweret	Goddess of pregnant women	Hippopotamus
Thoth	God of knowledge and writing – the scribe of the gods	Ibis

Note:

You may find that attributes and symbols change, depending on the source material.

Eight ways to help ...

There are hundreds of ideas in this book to enable you to develop and extend the photocopiable pages. Here are just eight ways to help you make the most of the **Ideas Bank** series.

1 Photocopy a page, paste on to card and laminate/cover with sticky-backed plastic to use with groups. Children can now write on the pages using water-based pens and this can be washed off.

2 Photocopy on to both sides of the paper. Put another useful activity on the back. Develop a simple filing system so others can find relevant sheets and do not duplicate them again.

7 Make an overhead transparency of the page. You and your colleagues can now use the idea time and time again.

3 Save the sheets - if the children do not have to cut them up as a part of the activity - and re-use. Label the sets, and keep them safely in files.

8 Ask yourself, 'Does every child in this class/group need to deal with/work through this photocopiable sheet?' If not, don't photocopy it!

6 Use as an ideas page for yourself. Discuss issues with the class and get children to produce artwork and writing.

4 Make the most of group work. Children working in small groups need one sheet to discuss between them.

5 Put the sheets inside clear plastic wallets. This means the sheets are easily stored in a binder and will last longer. Children's writing can again be wiped away.